All-Time
GREAT DUETS

SECTION 1
POP DUETS

SECTION 2
SHOW DUETS

WISE PUBLICATIONS
PART OF THE MUSIC SALES GROUP
LONDON / NEW YORK / PARIS / SYDNEY / COPENHAGEN / BERLIN / MADRID / HONG KONG / TOKYO

Published by
Wise Publications
14-15 Berners Street, London W1T 3LJ

Exclusive Distributors:
Music Sales Limited
Distribution Centre, Newmarket Road,
Bury St Edmunds, Suffolk IP33 3YB, UK.
Music Sales Pty Limited
20 Resolution Drive, Caringbah, NSW 2229, Australia

Order No. AM1004465
ISBN: 978-1-78038-440-5
This book © Copyright 2011 Wise Publications,
a division of Music Sales Limited.

Music arranged by Paul Honey.
Music processed by Paul Ewers Music Design.
Printed in the EU.

CDs recorded, mixed & mastered by
Jonas Perrson & John Rose.
Backing tracks arranged by Danny G.
Vocals by Alison Symons, Alexander Troy, John Williams,
Jo-NasT & Cathryn Hopkins.

Previously published as *It Takes Two! 10 Great Pop Duets*
& *It Takes Two! 10 Great Show Duets*

Your Guarantee of Quality:
As publishers, we strive to produce
every book to the highest commercial standards.
The music has been freshly engraved and the book has been
carefully designed to minimise awkward page turns
and to make playing from it a real pleasure.
Particular care has been given to specifying acid-free,
neutral-sized paper made from pulps which have not been
elemental chlorine bleached.
This pulp is from farmed sustainable forests and was
produced with special regard for the environment.
Throughout, the printing and binding have been planned
to ensure a sturdy, attractive publication which
should give years of enjoyment.
If your copy fails to meet our high standards,
please inform us and we will gladly replace it.

www.musicroom.com

SECTION 1
POP DUETS

The Ballad Of Tom Jones

Words & Music by Thomas Scott, Francis Griffiths & James Edwards

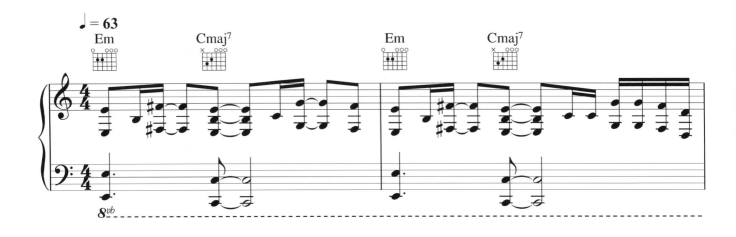

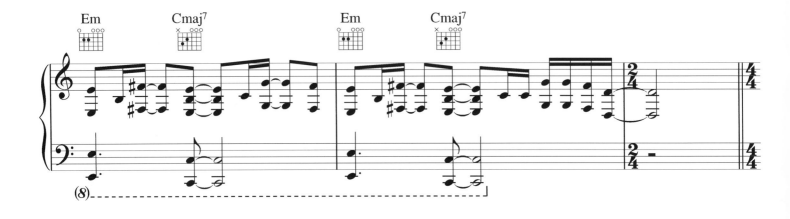

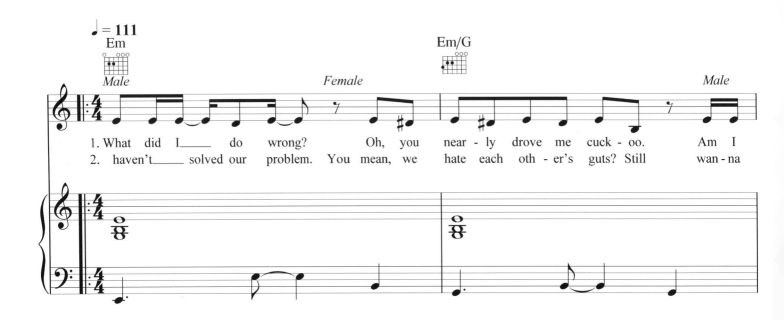

you'll nev-er know___ but you saved our lives.___ I have nev-er thrown my

knic-kers at___ you, and I don't come from Wales. You

You

Don't Go Breaking My Heart

Words & Music by Ann Orson & Carte Blanche

Don't Know Much

Words by Cynthia Weil
Music by Barry Mann & Tom Snow

17

18

Especially For You

Words & Music by Mike Stock, Matt Aitken & Pete Waterman

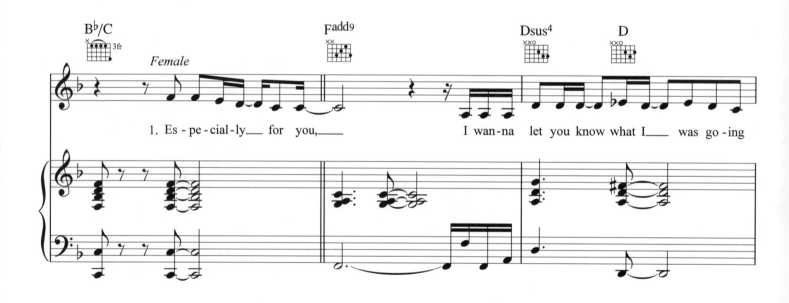

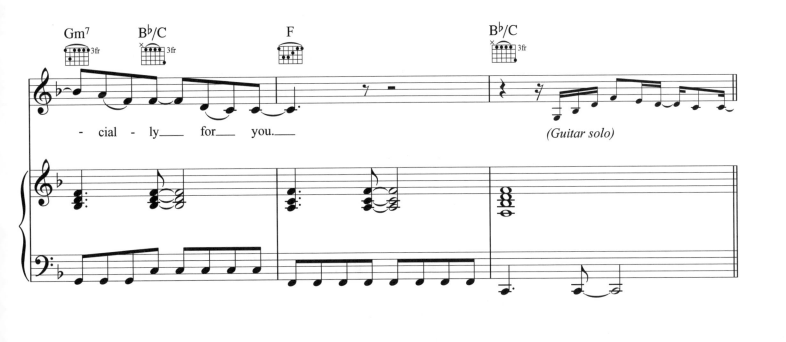

-cial - ly___ for___ you.___

(Guitar solo)

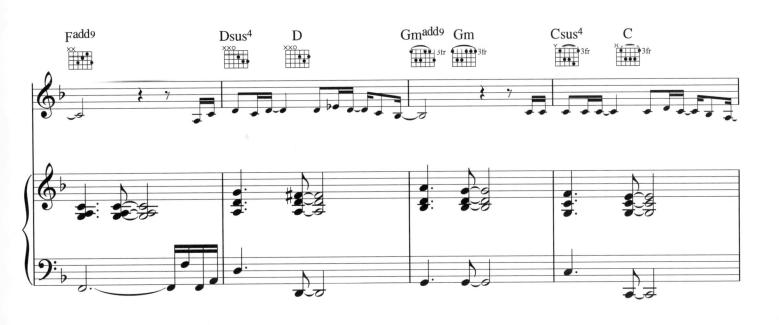

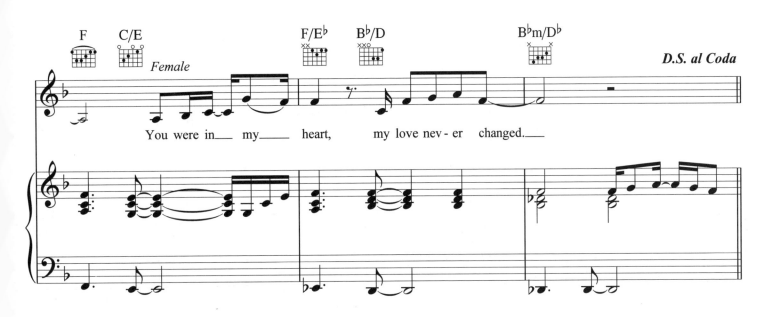

Female

You were in___ my___ heart, my love nev - er changed.___

D.S. al Coda

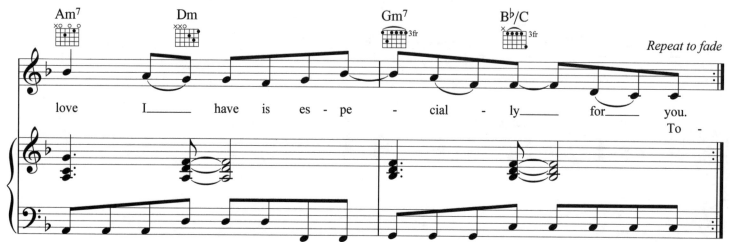

I Knew You Were Waiting (For Me)

Words & Music by Simon Climie & Dennis Morgan

28

Islands In The Stream

Words & Music by Barry Gibb, Maurice Gibb & Robin Gibb

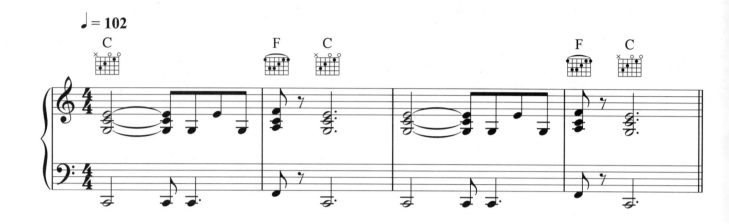

Ba-by, when I met you there was peace un-known, I set out to get you with a fine tooth-comb.__ I was

soft in-side,__ there__ was some-thing go-ing on.__

A Little Time

Words & Music by Paul Heaton & David Rotheray

time____ to find my free - dom.____ I need a lit - tle...
room____ all____ a - lone_____ I need a lit - tle... You
time____ and I still love__ you__ I've had a lit - tle... You

Fun - ny how quick the milk__ turns sour,____ is - n't it, is - n't it? Your
need a lit - tle room for your__ big head,__ don't_ you, don't_ you? You
had a lit - tle time and you had a lit - tle fun,__ did -n't you, did -n't you? When

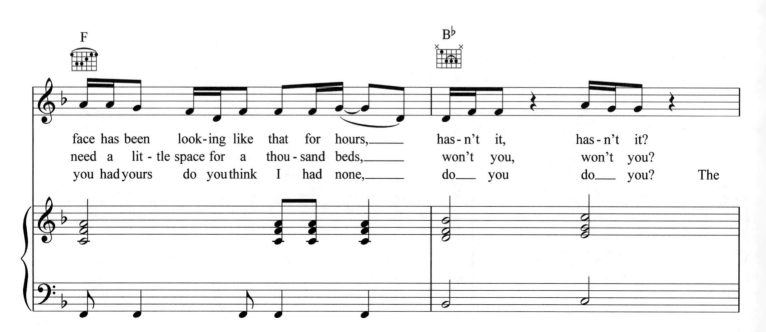

face has been look - ing like that for hours,____ has - n't it, has - n't it?
need a lit - tle space for a thou - sand beds,____ won't you, won't you?
you had yours do you think I had none,____ do__ you do__ you? The

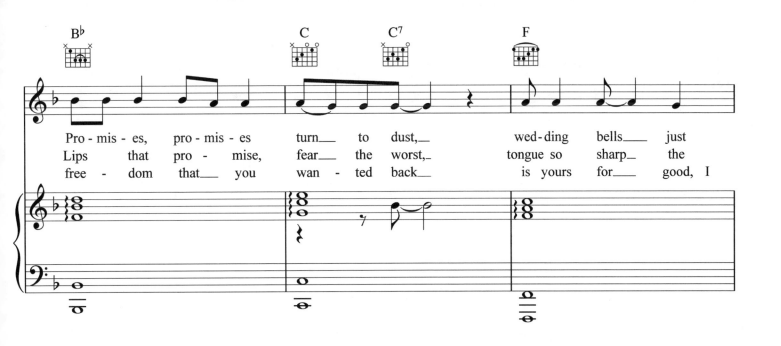

Pro - mis - es, pro - mis - es turn___ to dust,___ wed - ding bells___ just
Lips that pro - mise, fear___ the worst,___ tongue so sharp___ the
free - dom that___ you wan - ted back___ is yours for___ good, I

turn to rust.___ Trust in - to mis - trust.
bub - ble burst.___ Just in - to un - just
hope you're glad.___ Sad in - to un - sad.

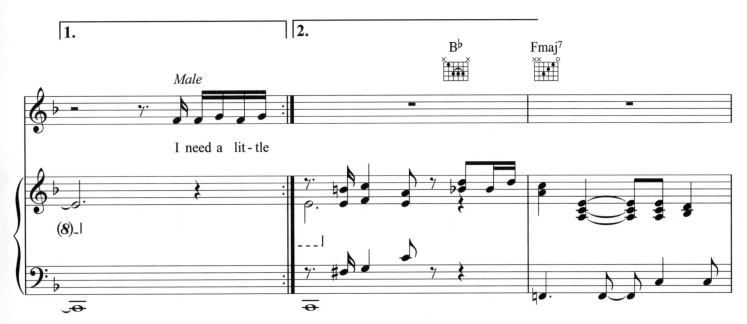

I need a lit - tle

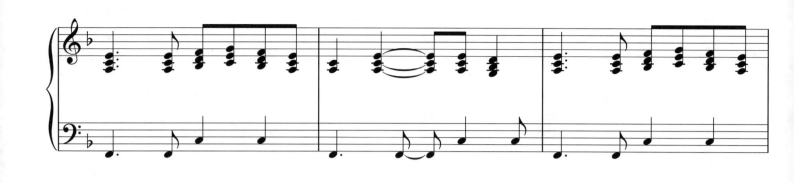

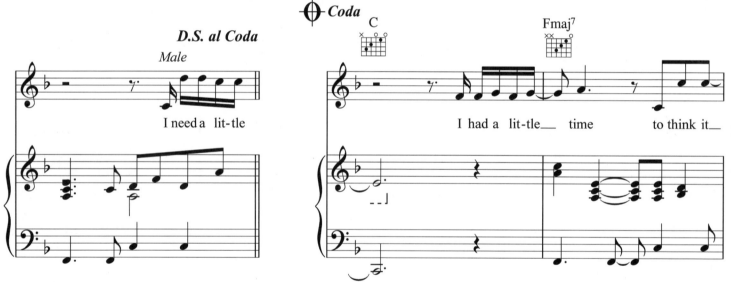

D.S. al Coda

Male

I need a lit-tle

⊕ Coda

I had a lit-tle___ time   to think it___

___ ov - er.___ Had a lit-tle___ room___ to work_ it out.___ I found a lit-tle___

Kids

Words & Music by Robbie Williams & Guy Chambers

1. Me no bub-bl-e-tious. Me smoke hea-vy tar.___

2. You've got a re-pu-ta-tion. Well, I guess that can be ex-plored. You're

I'm gon-na give it all___ of my lov-in', it's gon-na take up all___ of my love.

Female
Come down from the ceil-ing. I did-n't mean to get_ so high.___ *Female* I could-n't do what I want-ed to do___when my lips were___

___ dry.___ *Male* You can't just up and leave_ me. I'm a sing-er in___ a band.___ *Female* Well,

I like drum-mers, ba-by, you're not my bag.___ *Both* Jump on

On My Own

Words & Music by Carole Bayer Sager & Burt Bacharach

Somethin' Stupid

Words & Music by C. Carson Parks

The time is right, your per-fume fills my head, the stars get red and oh, the night's so blue.

And then I go and spoil it all by say-ing some-thing stu-pid like, "I love you."

"I love you." "I

love you." "I

123456789

All I Ask Of You
(from 'The Phantom Of The Opera')

Music by Andrew Lloyd Webber
Lyrics by Charles Hart

6

Do You Love Me?
(from 'Fiddler On The Roof')
Words by Sheldon Harnick
Music by Jerry Bock

Freely

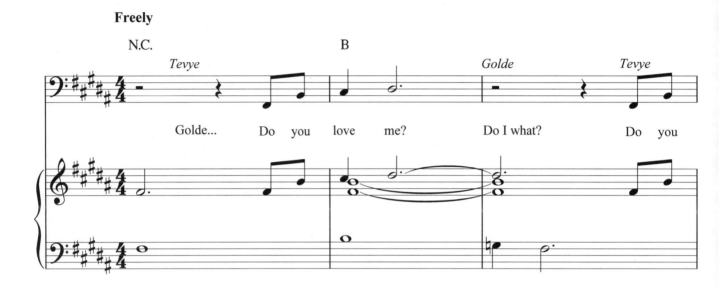

Golde... Do you love me? Do I what? Do you

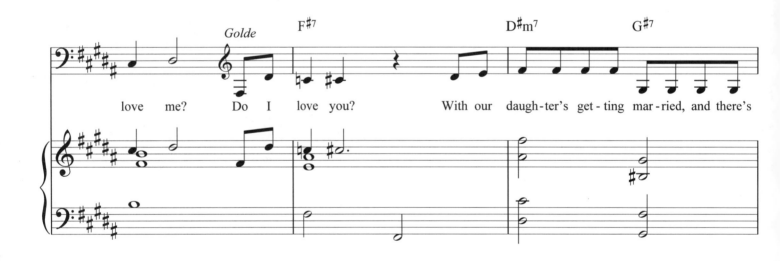

love me? Do I love you? With our daugh-ter's get-ting mar-ried, and there's

trou-ble in the town, you're up-set, you're worn out, go in-side, go lie down.

9

Golde *Tevye* *Golde* *Tevye*

on our wed-ding day, I was scared, I was shy. I was ner-vous. So was I. But my

Em · A · D · G · C#m7b5 · F#7

fath-er and my moth-er said we'd learn to love each oth-er. And now I'm ask-ing; Gol-de...Do you

B *Golde* *Tevye* *Golde*

love me? I'm your wife! I know! But, Do you love me? Do I

F#7 *Tevye* *Golde* D#7 G#7b9 C#m F#7b9

love him? Well? For twen-ty-five years I've lived with him, fought with him, starved with him.

10

I'd Be Surprisingly Good For You

(from 'Evita')

Words by Tim Rice
Music by Andrew Lloyd Webber

Moderato

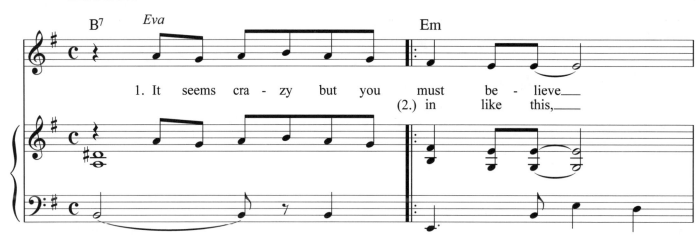

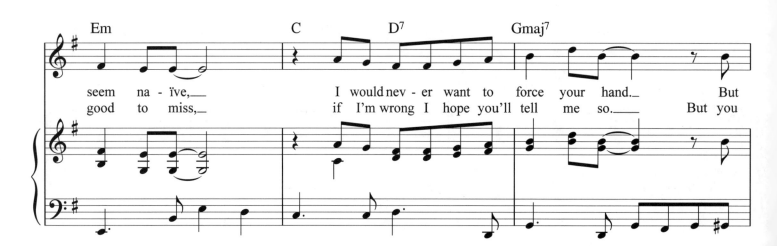

please un-der-stand, I'd be good for you.
real - ly should know, I'd be good for you.

2. I don't al-ways rush

I'd be sur-pris-ing-ly good for you.___ I won't go on if I'm bor-ingyou, but do you

un - der-stand my point of view? Do you like what you hear, what you see, and would you

be   good for me too?   I'm not talk-ing of a

hur - ried night,___   a fran - tic tum - ble then a   shy good - bye.___

Creep-ing home be - fore it   gets   too light,___   that's not the rea - son that I

caught your eye,___   which has   to im - ply I'd be good for you,

I'd be sur - pris - ing - ly good for you.___

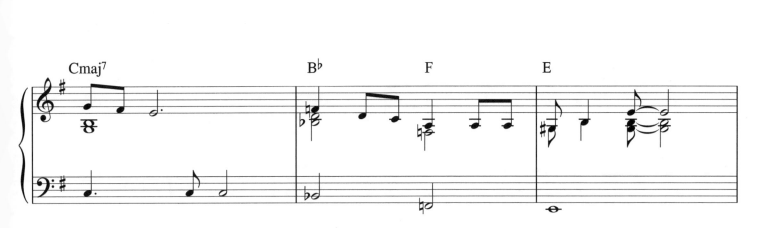

Em

Peron

Please go on, you en-thrall me!_____ I can

Am⁷

un-der-stand you per-fect-ly, and I like what I hear, what I see, and know-ing

D.S. al fine

B⁷ // rall. Em B⁷ *Eva* // a tempo

me, I would be good for you too. I'm not talk-ing of a

I'll Know
(from 'Guys And Dolls')

Words & Music by Frank Loesser

Money, Money
(from 'Cabaret')

Words by Fred Ebb
Music by John Kander

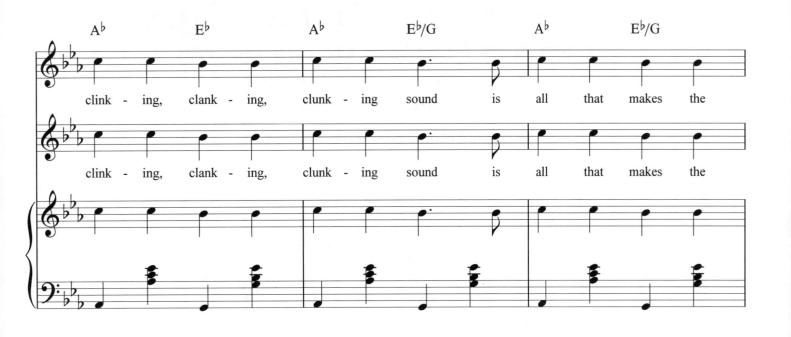

clink - ing, clank - ing, clunk - ing sound is all that makes the

clink - ing, clank - ing, clunk - ing sound is all that makes the

world go round. It makes our world go round.

world go round. It makes our world go round.

Repeat to fade

The Phantom Of The Opera
(from 'The Phantom Of The Opera')

Music by Andrew Lloyd Webber
Lyrics by Charles Hart

Allegro - vivace

In sleep he sang to me,_____ in dreams he

37

People Will Say We're In Love

(from 'Oklahoma')

Words by Oscar Hammerstein II
Music by Richard Rodgers

1. Why do they make up stor-ies that link my name with yours?
2. Some peo-ple say that you are to blame as much as I.

Why do the neigh-bours chat-ter all day be-hind their doors?
Why do you take the trou-ble to bake my fav-'rite pie?

Sun And Moon
(from 'Miss Saigon')

Music by Claude-Michel Schönberg
Lyrics by Alain Boublil & Richard Maltby Jr.
Adapted from original French Lyrics by Alain Boublil

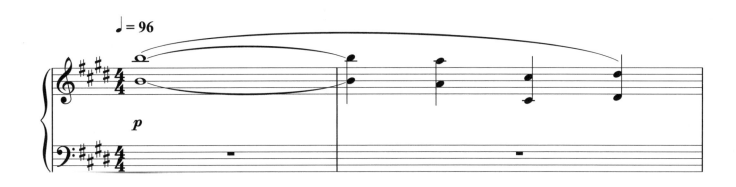

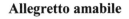

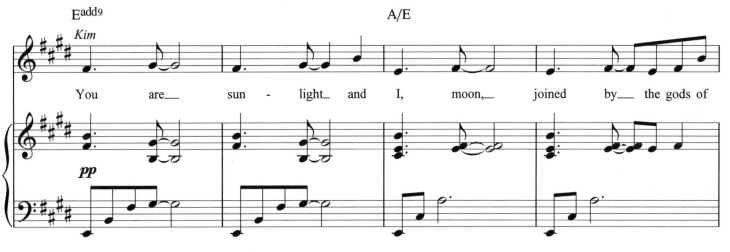

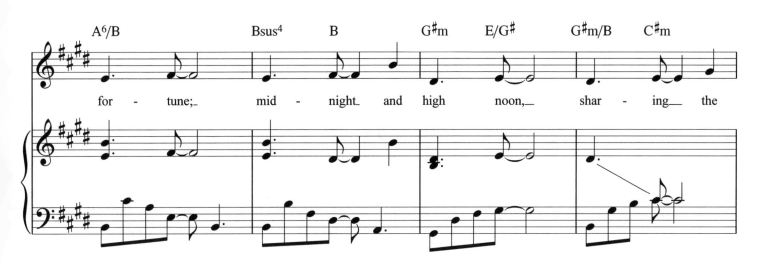

Appassionato

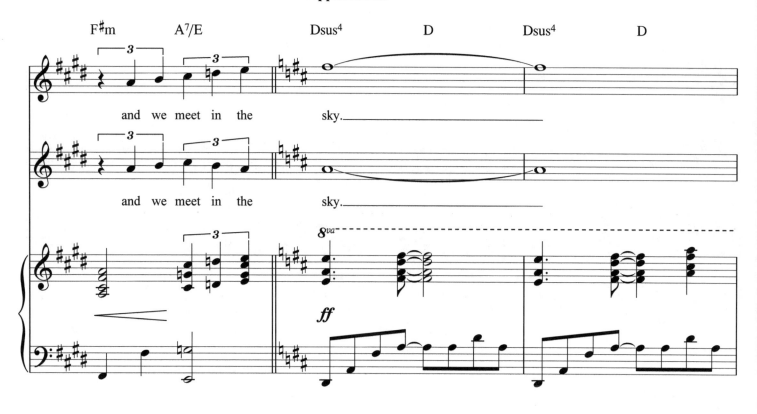

and we meet in the sky._____

and we meet in the sky._____

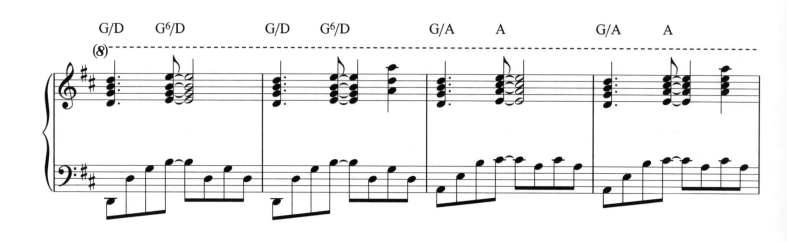

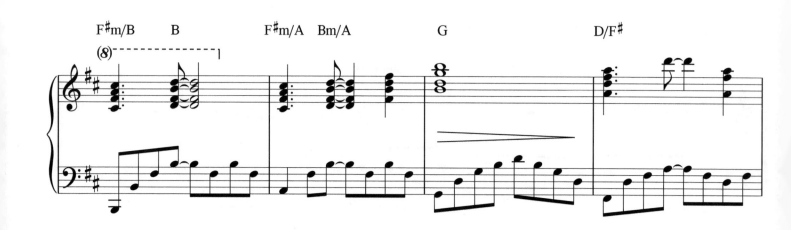

Why Do I Love You?

(from 'Show Boat')

Words by Oscar Hamerstein II
Music by Jerome Kern

You And I
(from 'Chess')

Words & Music by Benny Andersson, Tim Rice & Bjorn Ulvaeus

The Russian

Know-ing I want you,_____ know-ing I love you._____

—— I can't ex-plain why I re-main care-less a-bout you._____

Section 1: Pop Duets

Disc 1

Full performances...

1. THE BALLAD OF TOM JONES
2. DON'T GO BREAKING MY HEART
3. DON'T KNOW MUCH
4. ESPECIALLY FOR YOU
5. I KNEW YOU WERE WAITING (FOR ME)
6. ISLANDS IN THE STREAM
7. A LITTLE TIME
8. KIDS
9. ON MY OWN
10. SOMETHIN' STUPID

Male only vocals with backing...

11. THE BALLAD OF TOM JONES
12. DON'T GO BREAKING MY HEART
13. DON'T KNOW MUCH
14. ESPECIALLY FOR YOU
15. I KNEW YOU WERE WAITING (FOR ME)
16. ISLANDS IN THE STREAM
17. A LITTLE TIME
18. KIDS
19. ON MY OWN
20. SOMETHIN' STUPID

Section 1: Pop Duets

Disc 2

Female only vocals with backing...

1. THE BALLAD OF TOM JONES
2. DON'T GO BREAKING MY HEART
3. DON'T KNOW MUCH
4. ESPECIALLY FOR YOU
5. I KNEW YOU WERE WAITING (FOR ME)
6. ISLANDS IN THE STREAM
7. A LITTLE TIME
8. KIDS
9. ON MY OWN
10. SOMETHIN' STUPID

Backing tracks only...

11. THE BALLAD OF TOM JONES
12. DON'T GO BREAKING MY HEART
13. DON'T KNOW MUCH
14. ESPECIALLY FOR YOU
15. I KNEW YOU WERE WAITING (FOR ME)
16. ISLANDS IN THE STREAM
17. A LITTLE TIME
18. KIDS
19. ON MY OWN
20. SOMETHIN' STUPID

Section 2: Show Duets

Disc 1

Full performances...

1. ALL I ASK OF YOU
2. DO YOU LOVE ME?
3. I'D BE SURPRISINGLY GOOD FOR YOU
4. I'LL KNOW
5. MONEY, MONEY
6. THE PHANTOM OF THE OPERA
7. PEOPLE WILL SAY WE'RE IN LOVE
8. SUN AND MOON
9. WHY DO I LOVE YOU?
10. YOU AND I

Male only vocals with backing...

11. ALL I ASK OF YOU
12. DO YOU LOVE ME?
13. I'D BE SURPRISINGLY GOOD FOR YOU
14. I'LL KNOW
15. MONEY, MONEY
16. THE PHANTOM OF THE OPERA
17. PEOPLE WILL SAY WE'RE IN LOVE
18. SUN AND MOON
19. WHY DO I LOVE YOU?
20. YOU AND I

Section 2: Show Duets

Disc 2

Female only vocals with backing...

1. ALL I ASK OF YOU
2. DO YOU LOVE ME?
3. I'D BE SURPRISINGLY GOOD FOR YOU
4. I'LL KNOW
5. MONEY, MONEY
6. THE PHANTOM OF THE OPERA
7. PEOPLE WILL SAY WE'RE IN LOVE
8. SUN AND MOON
9. WHY DO I LOVE YOU?
10. YOU AND I

Backing tracks only...

11. ALL I ASK OF YOU
12. DO YOU LOVE ME?
13. I'D BE SURPRISINGLY GOOD FOR YOU
14. I'LL KNOW
15. MONEY, MONEY
16. THE PHANTOM OF THE OPERA
17. PEOPLE WILL SAY WE'RE IN LOVE
18. SUN AND MOON
19. WHY DO I LOVE YOU?
20. YOU AND I

Tracks 1&11: (Scott/Griffiths/Edwards) Gut Music Limited. Tracks 2&12: (Orson/Blanche) Warner/Chappell Music Limited.

Tracks 3&13: (Weil/Mann/Snow) Sony/ATV Music Publishing (UK) Limited.

Tracks 4&14: (Stock/Aitken/Waterman) Universal Music Publishing Limited/All Boys Music Limited/Mike Stock Publishing Limited.

Tracks 5&15: (Climie/Morgan) Warner/Chappell Music Limited/Chrysalis Music Limited.

Tracks 6&16: (B.Gibb/M.Gibb/R.Gibb) Warner Chappell Music Limited/BMG Music Publishing Limited.

Tracks 7&17: (Heaton/Rotheray) Universal/Island Music Limited.

Tracks 8&18: (Williams/Chambers) EMI Virgin Music Limited/BMG Music Publishing Limited.

Tracks 9&19: (Bacharach/Bayer Sager) Warner/Chappell Music Limited/Windswept Music (London) Limited.

Tracks 1/6/11&16: (Lloyd Webber/Hart) The Really Useful Group Limited.

Tracks 2&12: (Harnick/Bock) Carlin Music Corporation.

Tracks 3&13: (Rice/Lloyd Webber) Evita Music Limited.

Tracks 4&14: (Loesser) MPL Communications Limited.

Tracks 5&15: (Ebb/Kander) Carlin Music Corporation.

Tracks 7&17: (Hammerstein/Rodgers) Williamson Music Company, USA.

Tracks 8&18: (Schönberg/Boublil/Maltby) Alain Boublil Music Limited.

Tracks 9&19: (Hammerstein/Kern) Universal Music Publishing Limited.